Short
Islamic Plays
for Children

Book 1

Short
Islamic Plays
for Children

Book 1

Adapted by
Hassan Radwan

Illustrated by
M Ishaq

Short Islamic Plays for Children
Books 1 & 2

Adapted by Hassan Radwan
Illustrations by M Ishaq
Designed by Khaleel Muhammad
Edited by Tayyeb Shah

© 1999 Mountain of Light

This edition first published in 2000

Published jointly by Islamia Media (an imprint of Mountain of Light) and Ta-Ha

Mountain of Light Productions Ltd PO Box 7404 London N7 8JQ UK
Mountain of Light South Africa (PTY) LTD PO Box 43486 Industria 2042 South Africa
www.mountainoflight.com

Ta-Ha Publishers Ltd 1 Wynne Road London SW9 OBB UK
www.taha.co.uk

British Libary Cataloguing in Publication Data
A catalogue record of this book is available
from The British Library

Book 1
Mountain of Light ISBN 1 900675 39 0
Ta-Ha ISBN 1 84200 006 3

Book 2
Mountain of Light ISBN 1 900675 40 4
Ta-Ha ISBN 1 84200 011 X

Printed and bound by
De-Luxe Printers Park Royal London NW10 7NR UK
email : de-luxe@talk21.com

Contents

Introduction

This is a collection of short and mainly humorous plays that have been performed at Islamia Primary School in the London borough of Brent. They are a mixture of traditional and original tales that have been simplified and adapted for assemblies or as part of the school's annual Cultural Evening. Most of the plays here will take no longer than 20 minutes to perform and have a simple moral or message and so would be appropriate for Eid assemblies or as part of a cultural presentation. I have included only the basic script and a nominal amount of directions and settings, as this will inevitably vary, depending on who and where they are to be performed and the intended audience. Of course, part of the fun for children in presenting plays is dressing up, and most of these plays provide great scope for the imagination. Some are set in the past at the height of the Islamic Caliphate, while others are contemporary. Please feel free to tailor them to your own needs. I hope also that they can be read and enjoyed, simply as they are, by anyone anywhere. I would like to thank the teachers and the children at Islamia Primary School for their valuable input

General Tips

I usually begin by reading the whole play to the children to make them familiar with the story. Then I choose the cast. Some of the plays require a large group of children while others have a small cast. I know from my own experience of working with a class of 30 children, all eager for a part, that it can be difficult to satisfy everyone. One way of including more children is to put "helpers" or "attendants", wherever possible! At other times it may be best to explain to some that they will get a chance in the next play! Whatever you choose to do, it is a good idea to have a "second" or "stand by" who must learn the lines and be ready to step in if someone drops out. Once the play is cast, give them copies of the script and let them read their own parts. This can be done sitting down in the classroom. Try to get them to enliven and animate their part with how they imagine the character might speak and move. I like to get them to act out the whole play "without scripts" as soon as possible, perhaps by the 3rd rehearsal. By doing this they have to think for themselves and learn their lines. They will also develop strategies to help one another out if they see someone is stuck. As a last resort you can prompt them yourself. It doesn't matter at all if they don't repeat their lines exactly as they are written, so long as what they say flows with the story. In fact, I encourage children to come up with their own improvements or ideas that will enhance the play and give them more confidence. But always make sure that the story itself is not strayed from. Some children seem to be natural actors, while others need plenty of support and direction.

The basic rules are, always face the audience, speak slowly and clearly and pause between each sentence or line. You can even get those children who are having difficulty with this, to actually count up to three to themselves, between each sentence. Only when they have learnt their lines well and are confident, will they really begin to "act" and "enliven" the play. When you reach this stage it is best not to change or introduce new material as it will often only throw and confuse them. Now it's just, practise makes perfect! (Well nearly! - but that's half the fun, isn't it?)

Hassan Radwan

(Adapted from 1001 nights)

Baba Abdullah

The Moral of this play is that
greed only leads to misery & ruin

SCENE ONE   *Scene opens with the Caliph and his*
Grand Wazir Jafar talking.

Jafar   You sent for me oh commander of the
faithful!

Caliph   Yes Jafar, as you know I try to be a just
and good caliph and follow the example
of our blessed prophet Muhammad, peace
be upon him. Therefore I wish to know
what is going on amongst my people. So I
have decided to disguise myself as an
ordinary man and to go secretly out into
Baghdad and see for myself the state of
the Muslims under my rule.

9

Baba Abdullah

Jafar   But this is very dangerous, you might be harmed. If I cannot change your mind then you must allow me to accompany you to see that you do not get into any trouble.

Caliph   So be it, now let us disguise ourselves and be off!

They walk off stage, scene closes.

SCENE TWO   *Caliph & Jafar in disguise, walk through busy street, stop to listen to some men in a cafe.*

1st Man   It is good to see you again my dear friend, how did your trip go to the lands of the north?

2nd Man   Ah! We are indeed lucky to have such a wise and just ruler as our dear Caliph, for indeed in all the other lands I have visited I have found cruel and Godless rulers who cause nothing but misery and hardship to their people.

3rd Man   Yes, our Caliph is indeed a good man but I saw him the other day in a procession and I must say that the man walks just like a duck!

The men all laugh - even Jafar laughs, but the Caliph looks angry.

1st Man   Yes, it is true he does walk like a duck and he looks like a duck too!

The men all laugh again, Jafar laughs again, but the Caliph looks angry again.

Baba Abdullah

2nd Man	But he is nothing compared to his wazir Jafar, never have I seen a man who more closely resembles a monkey!

The men all laugh again - this time the Caliph laughs but Jafar looks very angry.

Jafar	(To the Caliph) I think we have heard enough from these fools, shall we move on sir?
Caliph	Yes, we shall walk down there.

They walk on and pass a group of women.

1st Woman	You know, my poor husband has been thrown into jail by that corrupt Qadi. He accused him of stealing from the good Caliph's treasury, but it is really he who is the thief. My husband is innocent.
2nd Woman	It is true, for I have a friend who works for the Qadi and she says she saw the stolen things hidden in his cupboard.

Baba Abdullah

3rd Woman   Why do you not go to the Caliph, he is a good and honest man?

1st Woman   I dare not, for the Qadi will surely deny it and hide the treasure, so where is my proof?

2nd Woman   And the Qadi will take his revenge and will have us thrown in jail, he has done it before.

3rd Woman   Oh, if only there was some way we could let our dear Caliph know without the Qadi finding out.

Caliph   (Turns to Jafar) Can it be true? One of my Qadi's is a thief and terrorises my good people and throws innocent men in jail! Jafar this must be investigated as soon as we get back, but take care not to let the Qadi find out until we discover the truth.

Baba Abdullah

Jafar	It will be done, insha-Allah, oh Caliph!

They walk past a blind man.

Beggar	Kind sir! Will you give charity to a blind man?
Caliph	Yes my poor man, here are two gold coins!
Beggar	Kind sir, whoever you are, please will you now beat me with this stick.
Caliph	What! Beat you with a stick! I cannot do such a thing to a poor blind man who has done no wrong!
Beggar	If you will not beat me then you must take back your money and forgive me for troubling you sir. For I have sworn a solemn oath that I will not take any charity without receiving punishment.
Caliph	But what have you done to deserve this?

Baba Abdullah

Beggar   I cannot tell you sir, it is enough to say that I deserve punishment.

Caliph   Then I must reveal my true identity, I am your Caliph and I order you to tell me why you took such a strange oath?

Beggar   Oh my Caliph, is it really you?

Caliph   Yes, this is my Khatam to prove it!

The beggar touches his hand and feels his ring.

Beggar   Then I must do as you command and I shall tell you my story. My name is Baba Abdullah. I was once a very rich merchant. I travelled to many countries buying and selling. I cared for nothing else other than the riches of this world. One day, as I was travelling with 100 camels through a strange land, I met a old man walking on foot.

Baba Abdullah

SCENE THREE	*Scene changes to a desert. Baba Abdullah walks in from one side and a very old man walks in from the other side.*
Old Man	Oh young man, can you help me and I will give you a great reward?
Baba Abdullah	What do you want old man?
Old Man	Not far from here is a great treasure of gold and precious stones. If you give me 50 camels we can load them up with more gold and precious stones than you have ever seen. Then we can go our separate ways.

Baba Abdullah

Baba
Abdullah   Well this certainly sounds fair to me. I agree to your conditions, now take me to this treasure.

Old man leads Baba Abdullah to cave.

Old Man   Come here and help me move this stone.

Baba
Abdullah   Wow! You spoke the truth old man, this is the greatest treasure any man has laid eyes upon, let us load up our camels.

Old Man   Now we have finished, could you just help me up to get a little wooden box that I left here?

Baba Abdullah helps him up.

Old Man   Now let us go our separate ways.

They say salaams, shake and go in opposite directions.

17

Baba Abdullah

Baba Abdullah   (Stops & speaks to audience) What does that old man want with such riches? He is old and will die soon. He does not need so much money. I should have more than him!

Baba Abdullah runs back to the old man.

Baba Abdullah   My dear brother! My dear brother! I was just going when I thought to myself, that you are not experienced with camels and will not be able to control so many. As for me, I am used to such a task. May I suggest that you give 10 to me so that you may travel safely? You will still have enough gold to make you rich.

Old Man   What you say has some truth, yes I will give you what you ask.

Baba Abdullah

Baba Abdullah (Takes them and walks 2 steps away, then speaks to the audience) That was so easy, I should have asked for more! I shall go back to him. (Runs back) My dear brother! My dear brother! I was just going when I thought to myself even 40 camels is far too much for a man who has no experience in controlling camels, as for me I am used to such a task. May I suggest that you give 20 more to me so that you may travel safely and you will still have enough gold to make you rich?

Baba Abdullah

| Old Man | What you say has some truth, yes I will give you what you ask. |

| Baba Abdullah | (Takes them and walks 2 steps away, then speaks to the audience) This man is a simpleton. I can easily take the rest of the gold from him. I shall go back to him. (Runs back) My dear brother! I can see that you are a godly man, given to prayer and charity and I fear that these riches will divert you from your religion. For great wealth is difficult to handle by one not used to such riches. Therefore, let me take this burden for you and let me have the rest of your camels. |

| Old Man | What you say has some truth, yes I will give you what you ask. |

Baba Abdullah walks away while speaking to the audience.

Baba Abdullah

Baba Abdullah	Now I have all the gold. What a fool that man is! (Stops and thinks) But I wonder why it was so easy? I wonder what is in that little wooden box, that he holds so tightly in his hand? Maybe it has a greater secret than all this treasure. I must have it! (Runs back) My dear brother! My dear brother! Wait a minute, I see you still have that wooden box, pray tell me what is in it?
Old Man	Oh, it is only some ointment that soothes my back pain.
Baba Abdullah	(Speaking to audience) He must think I am a fool if he expects me to believe that. (Speaking to Old Man) Oh really! Well, for many years now I have had a very bad back, if only you would give the ointment to me, I shall ask Allah to bless you and reward you.

Baba Abdullah

Old Man   I shall give it to you if you want, but I warn you not to put it on your eyes for it will make you blind.

Baba Abdullah   (Taking the box) Thank you and goodbye old man (The old man walks off). Now we shall see what is inside. (Stops in middle of stage and slowly opens the box in front of audience) It looks like ointment. (Puts some on his skin) It doesn't seem to do anything special. I bet he told me not to put it on my eyes because it will give me wonderful powers, perhaps I will be able to see all the treasures hidden in the earth. I shall put it on.

Baba Abdullah

Puts some on both eyes, then shouts!

Oh may Allah forgive me, I cannot see! Old man come back and help me I cannot see. My gold! My camels! Old man where are you? Help me! I shall die out here in the desert.

He sits and holds his head - then some travellers pass by.

1st Traveller Look here! What is this man doing out here all by himself with no means of transport?

Baba Abdullah (Standing) Oh kind travellers, have mercy on a poor blind man.

2nd Traveller We are on our way to Baghdad, we will take you with us.

Baba Abdullah

They walk with him until they take him home.

Baba Abdullah   Oh dear wife it is I your husband, a terrible calamity has befallen me, I have lost everything and what's more I have become blind!

Wife   What is this I hear, lost all your money and are now blind, but how will you work to bring me money?

Baba Abdullah   Is that all you care for, money, do you not care for me and wish to support me when I am in need?

Wife   I married you for your money just as you married me for my beauty, now you are blind you are useless to me, I shall sell the house and leave you.

Wife walks out.

Baba Abdullah

Baba Abdullah Oh if only I had taken our blessed Prophet's advice and chosen a pious wife.

SCENE FOUR *Scene returns to street.*

Baba Abdullah And so I was alone with no home and being blind I was unable to find work. I began to beg for food and slept on the street. But I swore a solemn oath that for every charity I was given I would ask to be beaten to remind me of my foolishness and greed. I have no one else to blame but myself.

Caliph (Speaking to Jafar) I feel sorry for this man, even though his greed has led him here. I can see that you have learnt your lesson and I am just sorry that I cannot restore your sight.

Baba Abdullah

Baba Abdullah   Do not be sorry oh Caliph, although Allah has seen fit to remove my sight, I see things I never saw before. I see that greed only leads to destruction. I see that the life of this world is nothing compared to the life of the next and I see that if you are content with what Allah has decreed for you, then you shall be happy.

Just then the Old Man walks in.

Old Man   I see also that you have learnt your lesson and therefore I shall give you this ointment which will restore your sight.

Baba Abdullah   (Rubs it on his eyes) I can see again! Praise be to Allah, Lord of the worlds! How wonderful it is to see. How true is the saying that one does not really appreciate something until it is taken away. May Allah keep us all healthy and grateful to Him!

Baba Abdullah

Whole
Cast   (Holding hands up as in Du'a)
        Ameen!

Baba
Abdullah   And keep us away from greed and love of
           the Dunya!

Whole
Cast   (Holding hands up as in Du'a)
        Ameen!

(By Hassan Radwan)

The Beautiful Island

The message of this play is that we are all different but can still live together in peace.

NARRATOR

Once upon a time there was the most beautiful little island in the whole world, just sitting there in the middle of the sea. One day a cat sailed up to the island.

Beautiful Island

Cat   What a lovely island! I think I will live here.

Narrator   *After a while a fox arrived.*

Fox   What a lovely island! I think I will live here.

Cat   Oh no you won't! This island is only for cats.

Fox   Oh yeah?! We'll soon see about that! (Fight - carefully choreographed!).

Cat   Alright! Alright! You can have that corner! Over there! But you must stay in your part and never come over here and to make sure I will build a big strong wall between us.

Fox   And you don't come over here either! (Glare angrily at each other).

Narrator   *After a while a horse arrived.*

Beautiful Island

Horse   What a lovely island! I think I will live here.

Cat   Oh no you won't! This island is only for cats.

Fox   And foxes!

Horse   Oh yeah! Well we'll soon see about that. (Fight).

Cat & Fox   Alright! Alright! You can have that corner! Over there! But you must stay in your part and never come over here and to make sure we will build a big strong wall between us.

Horse   And you don't come over here either! (Glare angrily at each other).

Narrator   *After a while a mouse arrived.*

Mouse   What a lovely island! I think I will live here.

Cat   Oh no you won't! This island is only for cats.

Beautiful Island

Fox   And foxes!

Horse   And horses!

Mouse   Oh please let me stay! I have nowhere to live.

Cat   No way mouse, we are stronger than you and if you don't go away we will beat you up.

Fox   Yes, we have no room for you so get lost.

Horse   Wait a minute. I feel sorry for the poor mouse, can't we let him stay over there?

Cat   Alright! You can have that little corner! Over there! But you must stay in your part and never come over here and to make sure we will build a big strong wall around you.

Mouse   Thank you! You are so kind.

Beautiful Island

Cat   Yes! And don't you forget who's boss!

Narrator   *Each animal stays in it's corner and glares angrily at the others.*

Cat   (Speaking to audience) I have the best house! Much better than the sly fox, the slow horse! And the titchy mouse!

Fox   (Speaking to audience) I have the best house! Much better than the slow horse, and the titchy mouse.

Horse   (Speaking to audience) I have the best house! Much better than the titchy mouse's!

Mouse   (Speaking to audience) I wish I had a better house.

Cat   (Speaking to audience) I need help with my maths homework, I wonder if fox will help me? She is very clever.

Beautiful Island

Fox   (Speaking to audience) I need help on my farm, I wonder if horse will help me? He is very strong.

Horse   (Speaking to audience) I need help sewing my clothes, I wonder if mouse will help me? She is very good at sewing.

Mouse   (Speaking to audience) I wish I had a better house.

Cat   (Goes over to fox) Listen fox, can you help me with my maths homework?

Fox   OK, but only if horse will help me on my farm.

Cat   (Goes over to horse with fox) Horse! Will you help fox on his farm so that she will help me with my maths homework?

Horse   OK, but only if mouse will help me sew my clothes.

33

Beautiful Island

Cat   (Goes over to mouse, with fox & horse) Mouse! Will you help horse sew his clothes so he will help fox on his farm so that she will help me with my maths homework?

Mouse   OK, but only if I can have a bigger house.

Cat   But that will mean we have to take the walls down.

Mouse   Well what's wrong with that?

Cat   What's wrong with that?! What's wrong with that?! I'll tell you what's wrong with that! I am a cat! She is a fox! He is a horse! And you are a mouse! We are different. We look different! We eat different food and we have different habits.

Mouse   So what? That doesn't mean we have to have walls between us, does it?

Beautiful Island

Horse	We can be different and still live together in peace can't we, without fighting and arguing?
Cat	Well I don't know. I'm not sure.
Fox	Let's try it and see.
Cat	Well…OK mouse! We'll let you have a bigger house and we'll take down the walls.
Horse	And perhaps we can even be friends.
Mouse	I think I would like that!

(By Hassan Radwan)

The Old King

This play teaches the importance of giving charity

In the palace, the Old King sits on his throne. His son and daughter sit on either side of his throne.

The Old King

Old King   It is time now for one of you to take my place and rule this land. But first I must test you both. I will give each of you 100 dinars. You must go out and multiply the money. Whoever brings back the most money will rule in my place. (Gives each a purse full of coins).

Prince   (Stands) Thank you father, now I shall go and multiply my money and I shall take my servant, Abu Saleem with me.

Walks off through town with his servant. A beggar approaches him.

Abu Saleem   Look sir! Here comes an old blind beggar.

Old Beggar   I am an old blind beggar, please give me some money.

The Old King

Prince	I cannot waste my money on you. I must multiply my money. Leave me alone.
	Walks on. Two children approach.
Abu Saleem	Look sir! Here come two children.
Two Orphans	We are two little children. We are hungry and cold. Please give us some money.
Prince	I can't give you any money, go and ask your parents.
Two Orphans	We don't have any parents. We're orphans.
Prince	Well I'm very sorry, I cannot afford to waste my money on you. I must multiply it.
	Walks on. An old woman approaches.

The Old King

Abu Saleem	Look sir! Here comes an old woman.
Sick woman	I am an old sick woman. I need a doctor, but I can't afford to pay for one. Can you help me please?
Prince	What will you give me if I give you my precious money?
Sick woman	I have nothing to give you.
Prince	Then you're no use to my money. I must multiply my money.
	Walks on. A captain and some crew members approach.
Abu Saleem	Look sir! Here come a captain and his crew.

The Old King

Captain & Crew	We are going on a boat to China. If you give us some money we can buy things from China which you can sell for a big profit.
Prince	Hmm...that sounds like a good way to make money. Yes, I will give you some of my money.
Captain & Crew	We will not disappoint you sir.
	Walks on and is approached by a merchant.
Abu Saleem	Look sir! Here comes a merchant selling gold!
Merchant	Asalamu-Alaykum! Do you want to buy some gold for 50 dinars?
Prince	50 dinars is too much, I shall give you 25 dinars.

The Old King

Merchant	You drive a hard bargain. Alright, I will give it to you for 25 dinars.
Prince	I have made a good profit!

Walks on and is approached by a shopkeeper.

Abu Saleem	Look sir! Here comes a shopkeeper.
Shop-keeper	I'm a shopkeeper. If you give me some of your money, I can multiply it and if you give me 25 dinars I will make it into 50 dinars.
Prince	That sounds good. Here. (gives money, then speaks to the audience) I have made some good deals, my father will be very pleased with me. I shall now return to him (exits).

The Princess now stands.

The Old King

Princess	Now I shall multiply my money and I shall take my servant Umm Ayesha.
	Walks off through town with her servant. A beggar approaches.
Umm Aysha	Look Madam! Here comes an old blind beggar.
Old Beggar	I am an old blind beggar. Please give me some money.
Princess	Oh you poor thing! I'm sure I can spare some money for you. Here have this.
Old Beggar	May God bless you!
	The princess walks on.
Umm Aysha	Look Madam! Here come two little children

The Old King

Two Orphans	We are two little children. We are hungry and cold. Please give us some money.
Princess	Do you have any parents?
Two Orphans	No, we don't have any parents. We're orphans.

The Old King

Princess	Oh you poor children, I'm sure that I can spare some money for you. Here take this.
Two Orphans	Thank you, may God reward you.

The princess walks on.

Umm Aysha	Look Madam! Here comes an old woman.
Sick woman	I am an old sick woman. I need a doctor, but I can't afford to pay for one. Can you help me please?
Princess	Don't worry, I will take you to the doctor and he will make you better insha-Allah.

They go to the doctor's house.

Princess	Doctor can you help this woman?
Doctor	Yes, but her treatment will cost a lot of money.

The Old King

Princess   That's OK. Here is the money. Now do whatever is necessary.

Doctor   Thank you, I will do all I can for her.

Sick woman   Thank you and may God always keep you healthy and well.

The princess walks on, then stops and faces the audience.

Princess   Oh dear, I have no money left. I had better go back to my father.

The princess walks back and is joined by the prince. Together they return with their servants to the Old King and sit either side of his throne.

The Old King

Old King   So what have you done my children?

Prince   (Stands) You gave me 100 dinars and I made many good deals and multiplied my money into 200 dinars.

Old King   Well done my son! You have multiplied the money twice. Now what about you my daughter, what have you done?

Princess   I have nothing father.

Old King   WHAT! But where is the money I gave you?

Princess   Well, on my way I met a poor old man, some orphans and a sick lady and I gave all the money to them.

Old King   Now let me think, (turns to Sheikh Abdul Mu'min) What shall I do Sheikh?

The Old King

Sheikh Abdul Mu'min	Well sir, the Qur'an says in verse 261 of Surah Al-Baqara (If possible someone can recite the verses in Arabic first): *"The example of those who spend their wealth for the sake of God, is like a grain of corn. It grows 7 ears and each ear has 100 grains in it. God multiplies the reward to whoever He wants and God cares for everyone and knows all things!"*
Old King	Thank you Sheikh Abdul Mu'min. (Thinks, then turns and points to the princess) I think that I will make you the queen!
Prince	(Stands up in anger) What! But I brought back 200 dinars and she brought back nothing.

47

The Old King

Old King No, she did not bring back nothing. She gave her money to the poor and needy and as we see from the Qur'an, God says that if you spend your money for His sake, He will multiply it 700 times! So she is the winner and she shall be queen!

Old King steps aside to allow her to sit in his throne

Princess (Standing in front of the throne) Praise be to God, Lord of the worlds!

(Adapted from a traditional tale)

Joha's Meat

This play shows how some people
take advantage of others

Two friends meet in the street.

Abou Yusuf Ah Joha! I have just bought this tender meat from the market and I thought that you and your wife would enjoy eating it.

Joha Oh that is very kind of you. Listen, why don't you come over to my house and share it with us.

Abou Yusuf Thank you, that would be very nice.

They go to Joha's house where his wife cooks the meat and they all sit down to eat.

Joha's Meat

Abou Yusuf Mmmm! That was very tasty, may Allah bless you and your wife. Well I must be going now Joha.

They give each other salaams. The next day two people knock on Joha's door.

2 People Assalamu-Alaykum Joha, you don't know us but we are the neighbours of Abou Yusuf. We heard about the tasty meal you cooked for him.

Joha Oh, welcome to my house. Any friend of Abou Yusuf is a friend of mine. Ya Umm Salama, bring my guests the dish.

Joha's Meal

2 People   That was very tasty, may Allah bless you and your wife. Well we must be going now Joha.

They give each other salaams. The next day four people knock on Joha's door.

4 People   Assalamu-Alaykum Joha, you don't know us but we are the neighbours of the neighbours of Abou Yusuf. We heard about the tasty meal you cooked for him.

Joha   Oh welcome to my house. Any friend of a friend of Abou Yusuf is a friend of mine. Ya Umm Salama, bring my guests the dish.

4 People   That was very tasty, may Allah bless you and your wife. Well we must be going now Joha.

They give each other salaams. The next day 6 people knock on Joha's door.

Joha's Meat

6 People   Assalamu-Alaykum Joha, you don't know us but we are the neighbours of the neighbours of the neighbours of Abou Yusuf. We heard about the tasty meal you cooked for him.

Joha   Oh welcome to my house. Any friend of a friend of a friend of Abou Yusuf is a friend of mine. Ya Umm Salama, bring my guests the dish.

6 People   That was very tasty, may Allah bless you and your wife. Well we must be going now Joha.

They give each other salaams.

Joha's wife   Oh Joha, these people are taking advantage of you. Are you just going to let them keep coming like this and do nothing?

Joha   No you are quite right, they are taking advantage of my good nature. But don't worry, I have thought of a plan to stop them.

Joha's Meat

Joha whispers to his wife.

The next day 8 people knock on Joha's door.

8 People   Assalamu-Alaykum Joha, you don't know us but we are the neighbours of the neighbours of the neighbours of the neighbours of Abou Yusuf. We heard about the tasty meal you cooked for him.

Joha   Oh welcome to my house. Any friend of a friend of a friend of a friend of Abou Yusuf is a friend of mine. Ya Umm Salama, bring my guests the dish.

Joha's wife brings in an empty dish.

8 People   What is this! There is nothing on this dish. It is completely empty.

Joha's Meat

Joha   Ah yes, you see oh neighbours of the neighbours, this dish is the neighbour of the neighbour of the dish that had food in it!

8 People   Well, what an insult we shall not come here again!

(Adapted from a traditional tale)

Joha Thinks He is Dead

The message of this story is that no one knows the future but God

NARRATOR

Joha is sitting on the branch of a tree and chopping the wrong end so that when he finishes he and the branch will fall down

55

Joha Thinks He is Dead

Traveller	(Walking by, stops to look at Joha) Be careful! If you keep cutting the branch like that, you will fall.
Joha	Will I really fall?
Traveller	Yes, you will certainly fall.
Joha	No I don't think so, I am sitting quite safely up here.
Traveller	I tell you, you will certainly fall!
Joha	We shall see, Mr. Oh-so-clever, know-it-all, Nosy Parker.
NARRATOR	*Joha continues to chop, while the traveller watches in silence. Suddenly the branch snaps and Joha falls to the ground.*
Joha	(Standing up and looking at the traveller in amazement) Wow! You must be a very clever man. You know many things.

Joha Thinks He is Dead

Traveller	(Looking pleased with himself) Well yes, I suppose I am clever and I do know many things.
Joha	You told me I would fall and I did.
Traveller	Yes that's right I did.
Joha	You know what will happen before it happens, you know the future. You must tell me when I will die.
Traveller	What, I can't tell you that, no one can tell you that.
Joha	Yes you can, you are able to see into the future, you must tell me.
Traveller	Look, I do not know, I am very late and I must go.
Joha	No! I will not let you leave until you tell me when I will die.

Joha Thinks He is Dead

Traveller   (Speaking to audience and shielding his words from Joha with his hand) This man is a fool but I will never get away from him until I tell him something. (Turns to Joha) Alright! I will tell you when you will die. One day you will be riding your donkey and it will slip 3 times, then you will die.

Joha   Oh thank you oh clever and wise one.

Traveller   You're quite welcome (laughs to audience and scene closes).

Narrator   *Many weeks have passed, and Joha is out one day riding his donkey.*

Joha   (Donkey slips) Oh my donkey has slipped!

Joha   (Donkey slips again) Oh my donkey has slipped again!

Joha   (Donkey slips again) Oh my donkey has
        slipped THREE TIMES! This is the
        dreaded moment. The moment I must
        die. Just as the traveller foretold. I shall
        now lie down under this tree and die!
        (Lays down and puts scarf over face).

NARRATOR *After a while an ambassador from anoth-
          er country comes by. Walks past Joha
          completely ignoring him and looks
          towards the town.*

59

Joha Thinks He is Dead

Ambassador   Now which road is it? Should I take the road on the left or the road on the right? (Turns towards Joha) Ah! Here is a fellow sleeping by the road, I shall ask him. Excuse me sir, which road is it to town?

Joha   (Does not reply).

Ambassador   What is the matter with you, are you deaf? I said which road is it to town?

Joha   (Speaking in a low voice as a dead person might!) Well, when I was alive I used to take the road on the left. (Points to road on the left).

Ambassador   What? Are you not alive now?

Joha   No, I am dead.

Ambassador   (Speaking to the audience) What a strange thing! A man who says he is dead yet he speaks. (Walks off towards towns).

Joha Thinks He is Dead

1st Guard	Halt, who goes there?
Ambassador	It is I the ambassador of Zumrudar, I have come to see the Caliph.
2nd Guard	Enter and may peace be with you.
Caliph	Assalamu-Alaykum ambassador.
Ambassador	Walaykum-Assalam oh defender of the faithful!
Caliph	It is good to see you. How was your journey?
Ambassador	Well it was fine, but just outside your town there is a strange fellow who claims he is dead and yet he spoke to me. Now I ask you, can the dead talk?
Caliph	Mmm! This is very curious, but I have a feeling I know who this odd fellow is. I bet it is Joha, he is well known around here for the funny things he does.

Joha Thinks He is Dead

Ambassador   Shall I show you where I found him?

Caliph   Yes please. (They go to find Joha who is still lying under the tree).

Caliph   Ah Joha! So it is you. What are you doing here?

Joha   I'm sorry to say, oh Caliph, that I am dead!

Caliph   How do you know you are dead?

Joha Thinks He is Dead

Joha   Well, a man who can see the future told me when I was going to die.

Caliph   Don't be silly, Joha, only Allah knows the future and only He knows when and where you will die.

Joha   But it is true I tell you, I am dead and it happened just as the man told me.

Caliph   I see, well if you are dead then can you tell me what is it like? Are you in Heaven or Hell?

Joha   Well, I'm not really sure, it is very dark.

Ambassador   You silly man, of course it is dark, you have your scarf covering your eyes.

Joha   I am dead I tell you! Please leave me in peace. Don't you have any respect for the dead?

Joha Thinks He is Dead

Caliph   (Winking and speaking to the ambassador) I think I know how we can raise this man from the dead! (He whispers to the ambassador, they then turn around speaking loudly to each other).

Ambassador   Oh well if he is dead, then we must take his poor wife and children into care!

Joha   So be it.

Caliph   Yes, and we must sell his house.

Joha   So be it.

Ambassador   Yes, and we must give all his money and possessions away.

Joha   So be it.

Caliph   Yes, and we must sell his donkey.

Joha Thinks He is Dead

Joha   (Sitting up and looking at the audience)
       Sell My Donkey?! No Way! You cannot
       sell my donkey!

Caliph   Aha! So the dead has risen!

Joha   (Standing and speaking to the audience)
       I'm sorry, oh my wise Caliph, I have
       been a very foolish man. But I have
       learnt my lesson, never again shall I
       listen to anyone who claims to know the
       future. Only Allah knows the unseen and
       only He will decide when and where we
       shall die.

(By Hassan Radwan)

Don't Hit Your Sister!

This short sketch was part of a presentation that dealt with the issue of smacking.

Ahmad   Hey, that's my ball! Stop playing with my things!

Sarah   No! Daddy says you have to share things.

Ahmad   But you never let me play with your things.

Sarah   Well too bad, I'm playing with this ball. I had it first.

Ahmad   Give it back.

Sarah   No, go away.

Don't Hit Your Sister!

Ahmad   You go away.

Ahmad hits her.

Sarah   (She starts to cry).

Dad and Mum come in.

Mum   What's going on?

Sarah   (Sobbing) He hit me!

Dad   That's very naughty Ahmad! You must never hit anyone! (He smacks Ahmad).

Ahmad starts to cry.

Ahmad   (Sobbing) Well, if I shouldn't hit anyone, then how come you hit me?

Dad   That's different.

Ahmad   Why is it different? I don't understand!

Dad   Don't you talk back to me my son or I'll give you another clip round the ear!

Don't Hit Your Sister!

Mum   Actually, perhaps we should show a good example? Perhaps we should not smack the children? Perhaps we should explain to them so that they understand?

Dad   OK!...look Ahmad, it is wrong to hit your sister, for a start she is younger than you and you may hurt her. Secondly, you must learn to share and be kind to others and Allah will reward you.

Mum   Now, do you understand Ahmad?

Don't Hit Your Sister!

Ahmad   Yes mum.

Mum and Dad go out together feeling pleased with themselves.

Dad   You are right. If we explain things then they will be good.

Mum   It is best to give love and attention to children and help them understand. That way they will become good.

After Mum and Dad go Sarah starts playing with the ball.

Ahmad   Ha! Now mum and dad won't smack me so I can get away with anything I want. Give me that ball you little brat.

He hits his sister and she starts crying.

Sarah   (Crying loudly) Mum! Ahmad Hit me!

OPINIONS REGARDING THE USE OF IMAGES AND ILLUSTRATIONS FOR CHILDREN

`Aa'ishah said, "I used to play with dolls in the presence of the Prophet ﷺ, and my girlfriends used to play with me. Whenever Allah's Messenger ﷺ would enter, they would hide from him. So he called them to play with me."

SAHIH AL BUKHARI, VOL 8, P.95, NO.151 AND SAHIH MUSLIM, VOL.4, P. 1299, NO. 5981.[1]

In the classic commentary on Sahih Al Bukhari, entitled Fat-h al-Baaree, Ibn Haajar al-`Asqalaanee wrote the following:

'This hadeeth is used as evidence for the permissibility of making dolls and toys with human and animal forms for the purpose of girls playing with them. This category has been specifically excluded from the general prohibition against making images. `Iyaad stated this to be categorically so and related that it was the position of the majority of scholars. He further related that they permitted the selling of toys for girls in order to train them for their youth in their household affairs and in dealing with their children.[2]

Ibn Hibbaan entitled a chapter in his saheeh, "The permissibility for children and women to play with Toys" and another, "A man's giving permission to His Wife to Play with Dolls", however, his not limiting the permission to child wives, is a questionable position.[3]

Aboo Dawood and an-Nasaa'ee collected this hadeeth in another chain from 'Aa' ishah in which she said, "When Allah's messenger ﷺ arrived after expedition to Tabuk or Khaybar, the wind raised an end of a curtain which hung in front of my closet, revealing some dolls which belonged to me. He asked me, 'What is this?' I replied; 'My dolls.' He saw among them a horse made of cloth with wings, and asked, 'What is this I am seeing among them?' I replied; 'Have you not heard that Solomon had horses with wings?' Allah's Messenger ﷺ laughed so heartily that I could see his molar teeth." This hadeeth is very clear that the meaning of playthings (lu'ab) mentioned in the earlier narration does not refer to humans.

Al-Khattaabee stated that this hadeeth indicates that playing with dolls is not like playing with other images which were warned about. And permission was given to 'Aa'ishah regarding them because she was not mature at the time. [Al-Khattaabee's] categorical statement [that 'Aa"ishah was not mature at the time] is questionable, however, it is a possibility. 'Aa'ishah was close to fourteen or past fourteen at the time of the Battle of Khaybar. As regards at the time of the Battle of Tabuk, she had definitely reached maturity by then. Thus the narrations of this hadeeth which mentioned Khaybar are more likely correct and they agree with Khattaabee's opinion, which is more preferable than the contradictions [inherent in those which mention Tabuk]'.[4]

Ar-Rubayya` bint Mu`awwath related that the Prophet ﷺ sent a messenger to the village of Ansaar on the morning of the day of `Aashooraa (10th Muharram) to announce that whoever had already eaten should not eat any more and fast the rest of the day; and whoever was already fasting should complete the fast. She went on to say, "Since then, we used to fast on that day and also make the boys fast. We would make toys out of wool for them, and if any of them cried for food, he would be given one until it was time to break the fast."[5]

The Islamic magazine, *al-Usrah*, published in Saudi Arabia grappled with the issue of figurative illustrations when they decided to launch a magazine especially targeted towards children. They wanted to provide an alternative to what was present in the marketplace, which had little Islamic contents and was introducing some unislamic values to their readers. They noticed that every single magazine for children printed in the Arab world as well as in the west was filled with illustrations of children, animals, etc. The reality is that colourful drawings are something that children are attracted to. If given the choice between reading a text with pictures and a text without them, they will always choose the illustrated text. The editors of *al- Usrah* thought of trying to address this situation by using drawings of inanimate objects with features added to make them look like live characters, but they decided that technique was too lim-

ited to use for the whole magazine.

In researching the Sharee'ah issues related to the drawings of living creatures, they reached the following conclusions:

1. *The basic rule regarding figurative illustrations is that they are haraam.*
2. *The reason for the prohibition is that it involves imitations of Allah's attributes of Creator and Bestower of Forms, in addition to the role of images in paving the way for shirk by magnifying the greatness of the illustrated beings, which leads to their being worshipped.*
3. *There is an exception to the general prohibition for children's toys, as is specifically indicated in hadeeth texts, due to the fact that the main reason for the prohibition is not present and that there is a tangible benefit in their use.*
4. *This exception to the prohibition of image-making is also applicable to whatever represents a tangible benefit, given consideration by the Shee'rah, or prevents or removes an expected harm, whether in the fields of education, public safety or other areas.*
5. *Pictures drawn specially for children enter into the exception, by analogy with children's dolls and toys, on the one hand, and in order to realise the benefits recognised by the Sharee'ah and due to the pressing need for*

them in contemporary children's stories, on the other.

In this regard Shaykh Naasiruddeen al-Albaanee stated in his book, Addab az-Zafaaf, "These two hadeeths (the hadeeth of `Aa'ishah's dolls and the hadeeth about the Sahaabah's practice of giving their fasting children toy figures to distract them from their hunger) indicate the permissibility of creating images and owning them when their is an educational benefit in doing so, one that will help in the cultivation and development of the personality. Whatever else is of benefit to the Muslims and Islam may be included in the same ruling of permissibility of picture making and use, but everything beside that remains under the basic prohibition." [p.196]

In the same vein, Shaykh `Abdullah ibn Jibreen responded to a long, detailed question on image-making put to him by the editors of *al-Usrah* magazine by saying, "I have considered what has been mentioned in the question concerning the temptations and deviations to which the Muslim youths are being exposed both within and without the lands of the Muslims in the form of films and magazines, which are (so widespread as to be virtually) unavoidable, which have filled the Muslims' houses and palaces, and which cause Muslim children to imitate what they see and hear and read in them in their speech and actions, the contents of which are frequently evil and corrupt. [After weighing these factors,] I say: When an alternative exists to engage children and youth which is free, or relatively free, from such corrupt ideas and values, I see it as permissible, because among the basic principles of the Shee'rah is choosing the lesser of two evils in order to avoid the greater harm. Without any doubt, for Muslim children to be busy in reading Islamic magazines that include some pictures used to make the ideas clearer is less serious than their habitual viewing of movies and picture (magazines) that ruin their morals, pervert their innocence and divert them away from good. That is what is apparent to me, and Allah knows best."

Shaykh `Abdul `Aziz al-Qaari' (Imam of Masjid Qubaa' and professor of Tafseer and Qur'anic recitation at the Islamic University of Madeenah) had this to say about image-making:
"Regarding the Hadeeth of Aa'ishah that she played with dolls in the presence of the Prophet ﷺ, and, in some versions of the hadeeth, that one of the dolls was in the shape of a winged horse, and that when the Prophet ﷺ asked her about it, she replied, 'Didn't you hear that (Prophet) Suliman had a horse with wings?' to which the Prophet ﷺ responded by laughing; this hadeeth indicates the permissibility of children's figurative toys, owning them and using them, whether they are clearly representative or not, and whether skillfully or crudely fashioned. There is no basis in the hadeeth for making a distinction. Those who

say that Aa'ishah's dolls were not distinctly representative have made an arbitrary judgment not based on any evidence.

What do you say about a winged horse?

The variation in the texts on this subject, from severe threats of punishment to less severe threats and from the prohibition of the use (of wings) to allowing their use, indicates that the law revolves around the consideration of the accompanying benefit and harm. If the law was fixed on prohibition, far be it for the Prophet ﷺ to allow Aa'ishah to play with those dolls and that horse, all of which were three-dimensional images. From that we know that the rule is connected to benefit and harm. If the harm involved is dominant, as in the case of pictures idols and statues worshipped in place of Allah, or in the case of pictures of important or pious people hung on walls as a sign of respect, which is a major avenue leading to shirk, the rule is prohibited. On the other hand, if the benefit is clearly dominant, as in the case of children's toys, or images on rugs or pillows, etc., which are put to use without respect, then the rule is permissibility. Children's magazines, books and stories take the same ruling as children toys and dolls, since the benefit in toys and dolls is no clearer than that in these other (educational) media. This matter is not restricted to children either. Even for adults, it is permissible for them to employ images in all their educational and information media, as long as the benefit from such use is dominant over the harm."

Complied by Dr Abu Ameenah Bilal Phillips

Notes

1 See also Sunnan Abu Dawud, vol, p.1373, no. 4913.

2 Ibn Hajar stated here that some scholars like Ibn Battaal, held that the hadeeth of Aa'ishah was abrogated and that Ibn Abee Zayd related trhat Maalik disliked that a man purchase dolls for his daughter. Consequently. ad-Daawoodee also concluded that the *hadeeth* was most likely abrogated. Fat-h al-Baaree, vol. 10, p. 544.

3 Ibn Hajar added here that al-Bayhaqee, after narrating this hadeeth stated that the prohibition against making images is undeniable / unshakeable, therefore this permission to 'Aa'ishah should be considered as having taken place before the prohibition. Ibn al-Jawzee catergorically held that this was the correct position. Al-Munthiree stated that if the toys were image-like, the permission to 'Aa'ishah must have been before the prohibition. Otherwise, playthings without images may also be called toys/dolls. Al-Haleemee stated catergorically that if the toy has an image like an idol, it is not permissible, otherwise it is permissible. After quoting ad-Daawoodee as saying *thatal-la'ib bi al-banaat* meant playing with "young girls" and that *bi here* meant *ma'a* (along with), Ibn at-Teen thoroughly refuted him. [Ibn Hajar went on to say that] the narration of Ibn 'Uyaynah related in al-jaami' from Hishaam ibn 'Urwah "... and some young girls used to come and play with them along with me," and that of Jareer from Hishaam "I used to play with dolls (al-banaat), and they were toys," collected by Aboo 'Awaanah aand others also refutes ad-daawoodee. Fat-h al-Baaree, vol. 10, p.544. Sunan Abu Dawud, vol. 3, 1373, no. 4914 and authenticated in the Saheeh Sunan Abee Daawood, vol. 3, p.932, no.4123

4 Fat-h al-Baaree, vol.10, pp. 543-4

5 Sahih Al Bukhari, vol. 3 pp. 103-4, no.181

GLOSSARY

Caliph	Muslim Ruler. Also called 'Commander of the Faithful'.
Grand Wazir / Wazir	Chief Minister.
Baghdad	A major city in the Middle East.
Qadi	Judge.
Insha-Allah	God-willing.
Khatam	A ring bearing the royal seal.
Dunya	This world.
Du'a	Making supplication to Allah.
Assalamu-Alaykum	Islamic greeting meaning 'Peace be upon you'.
Walaykum-Assalam	Reply to Islamic greeting meaning 'And unto you be peace'.
Allahu-Akbar	God is Great

A *is for* ALLAH

It took 20 years for Yusuf Islam to develop *A is for Allah* from a song to a monumental and attractive work. The book comprises of 68 beautiful full colour pages and over 40 photographs describing, for children and adults, the essence of Islam through the Arabic alphabet. The album on Double CD and Double Cassette complements the Book and includes:

**Hardback Book · Double CD · Double Cassette
Cover Poster · A is for Allah Song Lyrics Poster
2 CD + Book & postcard pack
2 Cassette + Book & postcard pack**

Audio version includes:

· COMPLETE BOOK NARRATED BY **YUSUF ISLAM**

· QUR'ANIC RECITATION BY RENOWNED EGYPTIAN QARI **SHEIKH MUHAMMAD GIBREEL**

· ENGLISH TRANSLATION READ BY **IMAM HAMZA YUSUF** FROM THE USA

· 8 SONGS - 7 ARRANGED & WRITTEN BY **YUSUF ISLAM** INCLUDING THE TITLE TRACK A IS FOR ALLAH - AND INTRO-DUCING **ZAIN BHIKHA** FROM SOUTH AFRICA

· GUEST APPEARANCE BY MALAYSIA'S WORLD FAMOUS NASHEED GROUP **RAIHAN** PERFORMING HARMONIES ON YUSUF'S SEAL OF THE PROPHETS

· ADHAN BY **MUAZZIN OF MAKKAH**

· APPROX. RUNNING TIME 101 MINUTES

POSTERS
594mm x 420mm

The Life of the Last Prophet ﷺ

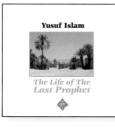

Yusuf Islam

With over 300,000 copies sold since 1995, this spoken-word recording of the life of Prophet Muhammad ﷺ was the first official release by Yusuf Islam since his departure from the music business as Cat Stevens back in 1978. The biography is fully authenticated and approved by an international group of 'ulema (scholars) and contains selected verses of the Qur'an, recited by the respected Egyptian Qari' (reciter) Sheikh Muhammad Al-Minyaoui. It also includes the song Tala'a al-Badru 'Alayna, and a beautiful rendition of the adhan (call to prayer) and is the best concise biography on the Prophet Muhammad ﷺ available in English.

Approx. running time: 60 minutes

CD £9.99 Cassette £4.99 Hardback Book
Giftcase - Hardback Book + CD
Giftcase - Hardback Book + Cassette

Prayers of the Last Prophet ﷺ

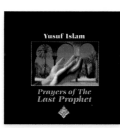

Yusuf Islam

Prayers of The Last Prophet ﷺ contains a collection of du'as (supplications) as used by the Prophet Muhammad ﷺ. Narrated by Yusuf Islam and structured around phases of the day, these du'as cover a range of everyday activities seeking God's guidance. All are derived from Qur'an and Hadith and are fully authenticated. Prayers also contains Qur'anic recitation by the acclaimed Egyptian Qari' (reciter) the late Sheikh Mahmoud Khalil Alhousari and features 3 new songs including Yusuf Islam's If You Ask Me.

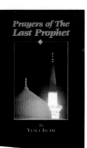

Approx. running time: 60 minutes

CD Cassette Hardback Book
Giftcase - Hardback Book + CD
Giftcase - Hardback Book + Cassette

30th Juz *of the* Holy Qur'an

In English & Arabic

Arabic recitation by Sheikh Muhammad Al-Minyaoui

English narrated by Yusuf Islam

With Islam today having over one billion followers, the Qur'an is probably the most widely read book in the world, with sections of it being recited at least five times a day by Muslims during their daily prayers.

This recording features the original Arabic recited by the respected Egyptian *Qari* Sheikh Muhammad Al-Minyaoui with each verse being followed by its English translation read by Yusuf Islam. The Arabic recitation style is *tartil* and the English narration is based upon *The Noble Qur'an* translated by Dr. Muhammad Taqi-ud-Din Al-Hilali and Dr. Muhammad Muhsin Khan.

Approx. running time 120 minutes

Double Cassette

Double CD

 In partnership with Darussalam

'Qur'anic Alphabet'

Yusuf Islam

Using Qur'anic verses and pictures, 'Qur'anic Alphabet' takes us through the 28 letters of the arabic alphabet. 63 pages

Hardback Book
Paperback Book

Islamic Teachings Course

Volumes 1, 2 & 3

Presented by the well respected scholar Jamal Badawi, *Islamic Teachings Course* Volumes 1,2 & 3, answers hundreds of questions on Islam in a simple paper-back format.

Vol. 2 124pp
Vol. 2 80pp
Vol. 3 133pp

THE SYLLABUSES
Islamia Primary School

The Syllabuses contain all National Curriculum subjects together with Arabic, Qur'an and Islamic studies. They are presented in a durable A4 size ring binder with colour dividers and is designed to be updated. It is ideal for anyone involved in primary school education as well as parents.

12 subjects, 218pp

(Individual subjects also available)

OFFICIAL UK VERSION

RAIHAN

Raihan are the best nasheed (song) group in the world! Having taken Malaysia by storm, they have quickly gone on to achieve international acclaim. Singing in Malay, Arabic and English, and with songs full of fantastic harmonies, they have redefined Islamic nasheeds. Jamal Records is proud to present the official UK versions of *Puji Pujian* and *Syukur* which come complete with English sleeve notes and lyrics.

PUJI PUJIAN

Their premier album made them big, selling over 650,000 copies and features the hit tracks *Rakan Selawat (Maulid)* and *Assolatuwasalam*.

CD

Cassette

SYUKUR

Syukur, their second album, contains 2 songs by Yusuf Islam including the exquisite *God is the Light*.

CD

Cassette

In partnership with *wea* ZAMRUD

Khaleel Muhammad

Ever wanted something for the kids that was hip, entertaining AND with Islamic morals??? Well, have no fear Hakim our intrepid 13-year-old Muslim hero is here!

the adventures of HAKIM

Written and read by Khaleel Muhammad, *The Adventures of Hakim* is a great audio-book for the young and the young at heart and includes the catchy song 'Streetwise Believer'.

Approx. running time: 61 minutes

Double Cassette music
Double Cassette non-music

Ta-Ha Publishers Ltd.

email : sales@taha.co.uk

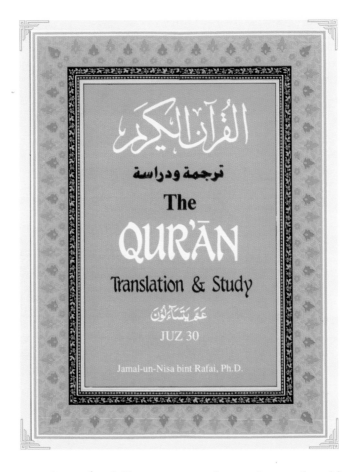

young students should be encouraged to understand and learn the meaning of the *surahs* which they regularly recite in their daily prayers. From *Surat'an-Naba* to *Surat'an-Nas*.

146pp Paperback A4

ISBN 1 897940 35 1

£ 5.00